Copyright © ticktock Entertainment Ltd 2009

First published in Great Britain in 2009 by ticktock Media Ltd,
The Old Sawmill, 103 Goods Station Road, Tunbridge Wells, Kent, TN1 2DP

ticktock project editor: Ruth Owen
ticktock project designer: Sara Greasley
With thanks to: Sally Morgan, Trudi Webb, Jean Coppendale and Elizabeth Wiggans

ISBN 978-1-84696-989-8 pbk

Printed in China

Picture credits (t=top; b=bottom; c=centre; l=left; r=right):
Ardea: 26c. Wendy Blanshard, Australian Koala Foundation, www.savethekoala.com www.savethekoala.com: 24t. Corbis: 18 main,
19t, 29t, 34c, 42tl, 44c. FLPA: 8t, 11 main, 13tl, 14tl, 14c, 19b, 22c, 24 main, 39cl, 39tl, 41t, 41r, 43b, 46b, 47t, 47b, 51cl, 52b, 57b,
58b, 62, 63, 66, 67, 69t, 72b, 73t, 74b, 75b, 79b, 82c, 89t, 89c, 90-91 (all). Thomas Dressler/ardea.com: OFC. iStock: 5b, OBC tc,
OBC br. Nature Picture Library: 9t, 14-15 main, 48, 49, 61cr, 61cl, 83t, 87tr. NHPA: 28b, 44c, 60cl, 65b, 93t.
Oxford Scientific Photo Library: 15t, 16c. Shutterstock: 1, 2, 4 (all), 5t, 6-7, 8tl, 8tr, 9b, 10t, 10 main, 11t, 12 (all), 12-13c, 13tr, 13cr,
13b, 18tl, 20tl, 21t, 21 main, 22tl, 22-23 main, 23t, 24tl, 25t, 25b, 26tl, 27b, 28tl, 29 main, 30-31, 32tl, 32-33 main, 32b, 33t, 34tl,
35t, 35b, 36 (all), 37, 38 (all), 38-39c, 39cr, 39b, 40tl, 44tl, 45, 46tl, 50 (all), 51r, 52tl, 53 (all), 54-55, 56tl, 56c, 57t, 58tl, 59t, 59b,
60ct, 60cr, 60b, 61b, 61t, 64 main, 65t, 68tl, 68b, 69b, 70-71, 74t, 76tl, 76b, 77, 78, 80-81 (all), 84 (all), 86-87, 88tl, 88-89b, 92tl,
93b OBC tr, OBC bl. Superstock: 8bl, 16tl, 16-17 main, 22b, 28c, 33b, 42b, 43t, 73b, 76c, 79t, 82tl, 83b, 85t, 85b, 92b.
ticktock Media Archive: 44 (globe), 64tl, 72tl, 75t.

Every effort has been made to trace copyright holders, and we apologise in advance for any omissions.
We would be pleased to insert the appropriate acknowledgments in any subsequent edition of this publication.

Contents

Introduction 4

Mammal Families 6

What is a mammal? 8

Mum meets dad 10

Amazing mammal life cycles . . .12

Pipistrelle bats 14

Giant anteaters 16

Orcas 18

Meerkats 20

Warthogs 22

Hippopotamuses 24

Koalas 26

That's amazing! 28

Bird Families 30

What is a bird? 32

Mum meets dad 34

Eggs and nests 36

Amazing bird life cycles 38

Hornbills 40

Emperor penguins 42

Arctic terns 44

Bower birds 46

Tailorbirds 48

Puffins 50

That's amazing! 52

Fish Families 54

What is a fish? 56

Mum meets dad 58

Amazing fish life cycles 60

Deep sea anglerfish 62

Salmon 64

Sticklebacks 66

Seahorses 68

Reptile and Amphibian Families 70

What is a reptile? 72

Reptile life 74

What is an amphibian? 76

Amphibian life 78

Amazing reptile and amphibian
life cycles 80

Nile crocodiles 82

Green turtles 84

Komodo dragons 86

Red-eyed tree frogs 88

Darwin's frogs 90

That's amazing! 92

Glossary 94

Index .96

Words that look
bold like this are
in the glossary.

Introduction

Animal families come in all shapes and sizes.
Meet the different types of animal family:
mammals, birds, fish, reptiles and **amphibians**,
and discover some amazing animal facts!

This feathery parrot
is a bird.

A zebra is a mammal. Zebra babies are
called foals. Zebras are pregnant for
about 12-14 months.

Seahorses are fish. Baby seahorses are
called fry. Seahorses are pregnant for
between 14 days and four weeks.

AMAZING ANIMAL LIFE CYCLES

A life cycle is all the different
stages and changes that a
plant or animal goes
through in its life.

Frogs are amphibians. Frogs lay frogspawn which develops into tadpoles after two weeks. They then grow into baby frogs which are called froglets.

Flamingos are birds. Baby flamingos are called chicks. Once the eggs have been laid, it takes about a month for chicks to **hatch**.

Amazing
ANIMAL FAMILIES

Mammal Families

What is a mammal?

A mammal is an animal that feeds its babies with milk. Mammals are also **endothermic**. This means their body **temperature** stays about the same no matter how hot or cold the air or water is around them.

This hairy cow is a mammal.

Most mammals give birth to live babies. When a mammal baby is born the mother feeds it with milk from inside her body. This is called **suckling**.

A hairy hippo nose!

Mammals also have hair on their bodies. A hippopotamus is a mammal with smooth skin, but it has hair in its ears and on its nose.

The leopard cubs in this picture are suckling from their mother.

Mammals can
be tiny like a
pipistrelle bat,
or enormous
like an elephant!

This pipistrelle bat is sitting on a scientist's finger while he studies it.

Did you know that people are mammals, too?

Mum meets dad

Koala dads don't help care for their babies.

Some mammals **mate** and then the male and female bring up their young together. Other mammals meet, mate and then the female is left to look after the babies alone or with other females in a group.

A male and a female meerkat will become a couple. They lead a family group and are the only ones in the group allowed to have babies.

AMAZING MAMMAL FACT
Meerkats live in big family groups of about 40 animals.

When a male and female warthog have mated, the male leaves. Adult male warthogs live on their own.

Male warthogs fight over who gets to mate with a female.

AMAZING MAMMAL FACT
Orcas stay with their mothers all their lives. They live in family groups called pods.

When a male orca is grown-up and ready to mate, he goes to another pod and mates with a female. Then he goes back to live with his mother in his family group. Female orcas bring up their babies in their family group.

The orca couple swim around each other – it's like dancing!

Amazing mammal life cycles

In this section we are going to find out about some amazing mammal life cycles – from orcas who live in the sea, to treetop koalas.

An orca

A koala

2

A female mammal gives birth to a live baby or babies.

1

This is the life cycle of a lion.

When they become adults, male and female mammals meet and mate.

6

Some mammals live with their family group when they grow up. Some go off and live on their own.

AMAZING MAMMAL FACT

A baby lion is called a cub.

3

Female mammals feed
their babies milk.

4

Lions are
meat-eaters.

Mammal mothers look after
their babies. Sometimes the
fathers help, too.

5

Mammals teach their babies
how to hunt, or find food.
Young meat-eaters practise their
hunting skills on each other.

Pipistrelle bats

Pipistrelle bats usually have one baby each year. Hundreds of female bats gather together to give birth in a building such as a church or barn. Sometimes they gather under a bridge or in a cave.

Father bats do not help look after the babies.

Bat pup

Mother bat

A baby bat is called a pup. When the pups are born the mothers and pups stay together in a huge group called a nursery roost.

LIFE CYCLE FACTS

A pipistrelle bat is pregnant for about 50 days. A female starts to have babies when she is between 6 and 12 months old.

A newborn pup will cling to its mother's fur if she needs to carry it to another place.

A mother bat can find her own pup among hundreds of other bats. She knows its smell and its sound.

This pup is suckling from its mother.

Pups can fly by themselves when they are about two to four weeks old. They leave their mothers when they are eight weeks old.

This picture shows bats in a nursery roost.

Giant anteaters

Giant anteaters live on hot, dry **grasslands** in South America. Adult giant anteaters live alone. When the male and female have mated, the male leaves.

An anteater's claws grow to 10 centimetres long.

The female giant anteater gives birth standing up on her back legs.

An anteater can use its tail for support like a third leg.

AMAZING MAMMAL FACT

The baby anteater is born with fur and sharp claws. It crawls onto its mother's back where she licks it clean. Baby anteaters suckle for about six months.

After a few months the baby hops off its mother's back to explore and then hops on again.

LIFE CYCLE FACTS

Giant anteaters are pregnant for 190 days. A female starts to have babies when she is about 3 years old.

The baby stays with its mother until it is grown-up, at the age of about two years.

If the baby falls off, it grunts to let mum know.

Orcas

Orca babies, called calves, are born underwater. They are born tail first. An orca calf can be 2.4 metres long when it is born!

A newborn orca weighs 180 kilograms.

LIFE CYCLE FACTS

Orcas are pregnant for 15 to 18 months. Females start to have babies when they are about 15 years old.

As soon as the calf is born the mother pushes the baby to the surface so that it can take its first breath of air.

The mother orca guides the calf to the surface of the water using her flippers and her nose.

Calf

Flipper

An orca calf feeds on its mother's milk for the first one to two years of its life.

The mother orca teaches the calf how to hunt and catch food.

Most orca pods have about 30 members.

Orca families talk to each other using grunts, whistles and squeals. Calves learn how to make these noises.

Meerkats

The meerkat's dark eye rings protect its eyes from the bright sun.

Meerkats live in groups that include males, females and babies, called kits. They live in **burrows** under the ground.

LIFE CYCLE FACTS

Meerkats are pregnant for 75 days. A female starts to have babies when she is one year old.

Newborn kits are helpless and do not have hair. They are born in the burrow and stay there until they are about three to four weeks old.

Female meerkats have three to five babies at one time.

20

Adult meerkats take it in turns to babysit while others go out hunting.

Meerkats stand up on their back legs to keep a lookout for predators such as eagles.

When the kits are about one month old, they start to go on **hunting** trips. Each kit has its own adult that teaches it how to hunt.

Warthogs

The female warthog gives birth to two or three babies at one time in an underground burrow. The babies, or piglets, leave the burrow when they are about two weeks old.

Warthogs use their good sense of smell to find food.

It is important that the newborn piglets do not get wet or cold. They sleep on a raised shelf at the back of the burrow to make sure they stay dry.

Adult warthogs and older piglets enjoy a mud bath to cool off on a hot day.

Warthogs use their sharp **tusks** to fight off predators such as lions. Both male and female warthogs have tusks.

Warthog piglets are not born with tusks. The tusks grow as the baby grows.

The piglets suckle for about four months. Male piglets stay with their mother for about two years. Females go off on their own when they are about 18 months old.

Hippopotamuses

Hippos live in a group called a **herd**. The herd includes one adult male, lots of females and their young. When a female is ready to give birth, she looks for a soft place at the edge of the river.

Male hippos fight over females.

The hippo baby, or calf, is born in shallow water at the edge of the river. The mother quickly pushes the baby to the surface so that it can breathe.

LIFE CYCLE FACTS

Hippos are pregnant for 8 months. A female starts to have babies when she is 9 years old.

The mother and calf move away from the herd for the first couple of weeks. This stops the baby being hurt by accident by one of the other adults.

An adult hippo can weigh 1.5 tonnes!

Most grown-up hippos stay in the herd where they were born. A male hippo may start his own herd when he is about 20 years old.

AMAZING MAMMAL FACT
Sometimes a hippo calf will rest on its mother's back. It will slip into the water if it gets too hot and then climb back on.

Koalas

Koalas are **marsupials**. This means that the mother has a **pouch** on her tummy where her baby lives. The pouch is a bit like a pocket. A newborn koala is called a joey.

The female koala gives birth in the eucalyptus trees.

LIFE CYCLE FACTS

Koalas are pregnant for 35 days. A female starts to have babies when she is 2 years old.

This newborn joey is about the size of a jellybean.

The newborn joey is tiny! It has no hair, ears or eyes. It crawls into its mother's pouch. In the pouch the joey drinks its mother's milk.

The joey's fur, ears and eyes grow. The joey gets bigger and bigger. When the joey is about six to seven months old it starts to ride on its mother's back.

Joey

At about one year old the koala leaves its mother. This is usually when the mother gives birth to another joey.

That's amazing!

All mammal mums care for their babies. They feed them milk and teach them how to find food. But mammal babies begin life in lots of different ways!

A baby giraffe is called a calf.

Female polar bears go to sleep in a **den** for the winter. While they are in the den they give birth to their babies, called cubs.

The polar bear's den is under the snow. Can you see the cub?

AMAZING MAMMAL FACT

The newborn polar bear cubs are about 30 centimetres long. They are blind, pink and hairless.

The mother and cubs leave the den after four or five months when it is spring.

The female platypus lays two or three grape-size eggs. The eggs hatch about 12 days later. The baby platypuses drink milk from their mother.

The giraffe is the world's tallest animal mum. The female gives birth standing up. The giraffe calf drops two metres to the ground!

A newborn giraffe can be 1.8 metres tall!

Bird Families

What is a bird?

Water birds, such as ducks, have waterproof feathers.

Birds have something that no other animals have – feathers! Other animals have wings, and other animals lay eggs, but no other animals have feathers. A bird's feathers help to keep it warm.

Flying birds have stiff feathers that help them to fly. They have small, soft feathers called 'down', for keeping warm.

Beak

Tail

Millions of years ago, **prehistoric** reptiles lived on Earth. These reptiles were the **ancestors** of birds.

Birds lay eggs like reptiles, but birds are **endothermic** animals, like **mammals**.

Scales

Birds have scales on their legs and feet, and claws like reptiles.

Flying feathers

Wing

Claws

Birds can be tiny, like the hummingbirds in this picture, or huge like an ostrich.

The ostrich is the biggest bird in the world. An adult male can be 2.5 metres tall!

AMAZING BIRD FACT
An ostrich is too heavy to fly, but it can run fast. Its top speed is 70 km/h.

Mum meets dad

A male and a female swan pair up for life.

Most birds **breed** every year, usually in the spring. Some birds stay together as a pair for life. Other birds have a new partner each year. Some females will have chicks with more than one male in the same year.

Tail

Some male birds have colourful feathers to attract females. The male peacock shows off to the female peahen by spreading his tail feathers like a fan.

Many male birds sing to attract a female to their **territory**. They defend their territory and their female by chasing away other males.

Peacock tail feathers are the longest feathers of any bird.

Some pairs of birds perform a dance together before they mate. The male blue-footed booby dances for the female. He shows her his blue feet and whistles.

The male booby spreads his wings and puts his beak in the air as part of his dance.

AMAZING BIRD FACT
To attract a mate the male frigate bird puffs out his bright red throat like a balloon.

Eggs and nests

This female swan is collecting leaves to put in her nest.

Many female birds make a nest on their own. Others are helped by their partner. Some birds make the nest before they mate – some do it afterwards. Next, the female bird lays her eggs in the nest.

Some birds make nests from grass, twigs or leaves. The flamingo makes a nest of mud with a **hollow** top.

The female flamingo lays one or two eggs.

The white stork's nest is made of sticks. The storks add more sticks every year, so the nest gets bigger and bigger!

The female stork lays up to four eggs in her nest.

Adult woodpecker

Chick

This great spotted woodpecker makes a nest in a hole in a tree.

This bald eagle is sitting on her eggs.

Female birds sit on the eggs, to keep them warm. This is called **incubation**. Some males help with this job too, and they also bring food for the female.

Chicks hatch from the eggs. Many chicks are helpless. Mum and dad bring food for the chicks.

In this section we are going to find out about some amazing bird life cycles – from the record-breaking Arctic tern to the friendly robin.

Arctic tern

Amazing bird life cycles

A robin chick eats about 140 bugs, spiders and worms a day!

1

An adult male and female bird meet and mate.

This is the life cycle of a robin.

6

When they are ready to go off on their own, the chicks leave the nest. Some parents teach their chicks how to fly. This is a picture of a young robin.

5

The parents bring the chicks food to eat. Some birds remove their chicks' poo from the nest, too!

AMAZING BIRD FACT

A robin's short wings are good for quick short flights from place to place while catching bugs to eat.

2

The female lays eggs in a nest.

Robins live in Europe, North Africa and parts of Asia.

3

The female sits on the eggs to keep them warm. Some male birds bring the female food while she does this.

4

The eggs hatch. Many chicks are blind and have no feathers when they hatch.

Hornbills

Hornbills live in the forests of Africa and Asia. The hornbill uses its large beak, or bill, to eat fruit, and to catch insects, lizards and snakes.

This is a southern ground hornbill. It feeds on the ground.

Most types of hornbill find their food in the trees, but some feed on the ground.

This great Indian hornbill lives in trees.

LIFE CYCLE FACTS

The female hornbill lays up to six eggs. The chicks hatch in about 30 to 40 days.

Hornbills nest in holes in trees. The female lays her eggs, then shuts herself inside. She blocks the entrance with a wall made from droppings mixed with mud and squashed fruit.

A female hornbill takes a last look before she blocks the nest entrance.

The male hornbill passes the female food through a slit in the wall.

The eggs hatch, but it may be three months before the female comes out. When the chicks get too big, she breaks open the wall, and climbs out. The chicks stay in the hole until they are ready to fly.

This is a male red knobbed hornbill feeding his mate.

Emperor penguins

Penguin pairs stay
together for years.

Penguins cannot fly. They use their wings as **flippers** for swimming in the sea. Emperor penguins do not build nests. After mating, the female lays one egg. The male holds the egg on his feet to keep it warm.

The new chick is warm on Dad's feet!

The female goes off to sea to catch fish. Sometimes emperor penguins walk for 100 kilometres to get to the sea.

All winter the male cares for the egg. In spring, the egg hatches and the female returns from the sea with food for the chick.

LIFE CYCLE FACTS
The female emperor penguin lays one egg. The chick hatches after about 65 days.

Big chicks stand in a huddle to protect themselves from snow and icy winds.

When the egg has hatched, the male and female take it in turns to care for the chick and go fishing.

Until their adult feathers grow, the chicks cannot swim. After four or five months, the chicks' feathers grow and they are able to go to sea to find food on their own.

The parent penguin coughs up partly digested fish from its throat, for the chick.

Arctic terns

Arctic terns catch fish
by plunging into
the sea.

The Arctic tern is the champion bird traveller.
Each year, this small seabird **migrates** from
the Arctic to Antarctica, and back again.
Arctic terns fly about 35,000 kilometres
around the world every year.

When it is winter in the
north of the world, it is
summer in the south.
Arctic terns fly south
to escape the cold
northern winter.
When the southern
summer ends, they
fly north again.

Arctic terns have two summers every year.

ARCTIC TERN MIGRATION ROUTE

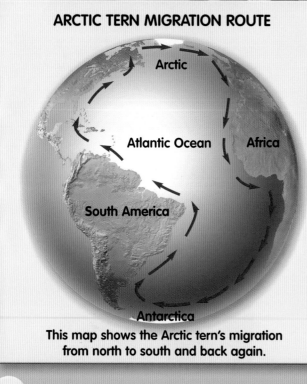

Arctic

Atlantic Ocean   Africa

South America

Antarctica

This map shows the Arctic tern's migration
from north to south and back again.

Arctic terns pair
for life. They mate
and lay their
eggs in the Arctic.

Chick

The parent terns raise their chicks during the short Arctic summer. When it's time to fly south, the parent terns guide the youngsters to show them the way.

LIFE CYCLE FACTS
The female Arctic tern lays two or three eggs. The chicks hatch after about 24 days.

The parents bring the chicks fish to eat.

Bower birds

Bower birds live in Australia and New Guinea. The male makes a little archway, called a bower, to attract a mate. He puts colourful things such as stones, bones, feathers or shells inside the bower. He makes a garden, too!

The satin bower bird has blue-black feathers and bright, blue eyes.

The male dances in and out of his bower. Females visit several bowers before deciding on a mate.

LIFE CYCLE FACTS

The female satin bower bird lays two or three eggs. The chicks hatch between 15 and 30 days.

Bower

Sometimes males steal decorations from each other's bowers!

This bird is taking a piece of blue Lego!

Satin bower birds like blue. A male may collect blue drinking straws, bits of blue plastic, even ballpoint pens!

Female

Male

This is a pair of great bower birds.

After mating, the female bower bird makes a saucer-shaped nest for her eggs. The male doesn't help – he is more interested in his bower.

Tailorbirds don't
mind people.
Some nest in gardens.

Tailorbirds

The tailorbird lives in south Asia. It makes a very unusual nest! Just as a **tailor** sews cloth to make clothes, the tailorbird sews leaves together to make a nest.

First the tailorbird chooses a long, wide leaf. Using its beak as a needle, it sews the edges of the leaf together to make a bag shape.

Leaf

For thread, the bird uses plant fibres or spider's web. It makes neat, tight stitches. Inside the leaf-bag, the bird makes a cosy nest of spider's web, bits of string and anything else soft.

Soft nest material

Stitches

This tailorbird nest has dried out. The chicks have left.

Leaf bag

The female sits on the eggs to **incubate** them. Both parents feed the chicks on insects and spiders.

Puffins

The puffin is a seabird that nests on cliffs. Puffins are excellent swimmers. Male and female puffins do a **courtship** dance – they bob heads and touch beaks. Then they mate out at sea.

Puffins eat fish – they can carry 10 small fish sideways in their beaks.

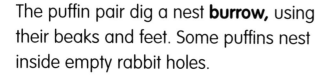

The puffin pair dig a nest **burrow,** using their beaks and feet. Some puffins nest inside empty rabbit holes.

A courtship dance.

LIFE CYCLE FACTS

The female puffin lays one egg. The chick hatches after about 40 days.

Burrow entrance

Inside the burrow the female lays one egg. Both parents incubate the egg and catch fish for the chick when it hatches.

When the chick is six weeks old, the parents leave it. After a week on its own, the chick leaves the burrow.

Nest material

Puffin chick

The chick rushes to the sea, usually at night, when there are few predators around. Rats and seagulls will kill puffin chicks.

That's amazing!

Swallows stick their nests to houses or cave walls, using their gummy spit as glue.

Birds are very good parents. They care for their eggs and chicks by building them a safe, cosy home and bringing them food. But did you know that there is one bird that's a very lazy parent!

The cuckoo lays its egg in the nest of another bird and then leaves it. The other bird does not notice the strange egg. The cuckoo chick hatches after 12 days and pushes the other eggs or chicks out of the nest.

The cuckoo gets all the food and is soon bigger than its new parents!

Cuckoo chick

Wagtail adult

Nest

Ostrich egg

Chicken egg

African weaver birds nest in **colonies**. Each pair of birds weaves a nest from grass and leaves.

An ostrich egg is the biggest egg in the bird kingdom. A hummingbird's egg is the smallest – it's about the size of a pea!

AMAZING BIRD FACT
Ostrich chicks are looked after by their dad – mum doesn't help at all!

Fish Families

What is a fish?

Fish are covered in scales that help to protect them.

A fish is an animal that lives in water. A fish usually has fins and **scales**. It can breathe underwater using body parts called **gills**. The gills take **oxygen** out of the water and pass it into the fish's body.

Fin

Fish use their fins and tail to move through the water.

Gill cover

Some fish live alone. Others live in big groups called **shoals**. A shoal can have hundreds or thousands of fish.

Fin

These fish eggs have been attached to an underwater rock by a female fish.

Most fish **reproduce** by laying eggs. The eggs are very small and soft. The female fish usually lays hundreds of eggs in one go.

Sharks are a type of fish. Some sharks, such as the great white shark, give birth to live babies called pups.

A great white shark.

Tail

AMAZING FISH FACT
When great white shark pups are born they are over a metre long and have sharp teeth, ready for hunting!

57

Mum meets dad

This is a pair of long-nosed butterfly fish. All butterfly fish pair for life.

Most fish reproduce every year. Some fish find a mate and stay together as a pair for life. Other fish have a new partner each year. Many fish **mate** with more than one partner in the same year.

Hammerhead sharks can live in shoals of over 500 sharks. The strongest female swims in the middle of the shoal.

When she is ready to mate, the strongest female starts shaking her head from side to side. This makes the other females swim to the edges of the shoal.

AMAZING FISH FACT
Sharks live in all the world's oceans. They have been around since before the dinosaurs!

Now the strongest female is the centre of attention and is sure to get a mate.

The angelfish pair in this photo are guarding their eggs.

Freshwater angelfish stay together as a pair for life. After mating, the female lays about 1,000 eggs on a leaf.

Eggs

A male emperor angelfish lives with up to five female mates. If the male dies, one of the females turns into a male fish and becomes the leader of the group!

Emperor angelfish live on coral reefs.

In this section we are going to find out about some amazing fish life cycles – from tiny seahorses to colourful lionfish.

Seahorse

Lionfish

Amazing fish life cycles

1 A pair of lionfish

An adult male and female fish meet. Some fish make a nest.

FISH LIFE CYCLE
Many fish have a life cycle with these stages.

4 Baby salmon

Baby fish called fry hatch from the eggs. The tiny babies take care of themselves. They have a yolk sac which they use as food.

2 Fertilised fish eggs

The female fish lays her eggs. The male fish covers the eggs with a liquid from his body called sperm. Now the eggs are fertilised.

3 A pair of angelfish

Some fish guard their eggs. Others leave them to hatch on their own.

1

A pair of nurse sharks

An adult male and female shark meet and mate.

3

2

A black tip shark pup

SHARK LIFE CYCLE
Some sharks have a life cycle with these stages.

A female lemon shark and pups

As soon as they are born, the pups take care of themselves. They have teeth and are ready to hunt.

The female shark gives birth to lots of pups at the same time.

AMAZING FISH FACT

This is a pair of red flower horn fish. There are about 24,500 different types of fish.

Deep sea anglerfish

Anglerfish live at the very bottom of deep oceans where it is very dark. The female has a long spine which comes out of her head. On the end is a ball that can glow like a light.

The female anglerfish can open her mouth really wide to eat fish the same size as her.

The female anglerfish uses her light to attract other fish – then she eats them!

Light

The male anglerfish cannot feed himself. As soon as he is old enough he has to find a female to live with.

The small male attaches himself to a female. They stay together for life. The male gets smaller and smaller.

Female

Male

When it is time to reproduce and lay eggs, the female already has her mate with her.

Salmon

Adult salmon live in the oceans. In the autumn, when it is time to mate and lay eggs, they have to swim back to the freshwater river where they were born.

A salmon who is ready to reproduce is called a spawner.

The salmon have a dangerous journey. They have to swim a long way and they swim **upstream** which is very tiring.

AMAZING FISH FACT
The salmon have to leap up waterfalls and avoid predators such as grizzly bears.

Grizzly bears

Salmon

When a female salmon reaches the spawning ground she makes four or five nests called redds. She lays about 1,000 eggs in each nest. Then a male fertilises the eggs.

Thousands of spawners gather in the same place.

The eggs hatch after four months. The small salmon are called alevins. They have an orange yolk sac which contains all the food they will need to grow.

Egg

Alevin

The young salmon grow bigger and bigger. After about three years they are ready to swim out to sea.

Yolk sac

Sticklebacks feed on tiny shellfish and the fry and eggs of other fish.

Sticklebacks

Sticklebacks are tiny fish – they grow to just five centimetres long. Some sticklebacks live in **saltwater** close to the **coast**. Others live in freshwater ponds, lakes and rivers.

Nest

Between March and August the male stickleback changes colour to attract a mate.

Then the male stickleback builds a nest from bits of plant. He does a zigzag dance in front of the nest to attract a female.

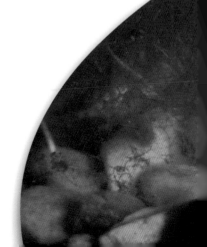

During the mating season, the underside of the male's body becomes a bright orange-red colour, his eyes turn blue and silver scales appear on his back.

Lots of different females lay their eggs in the male's nest. Then he fertilises them.

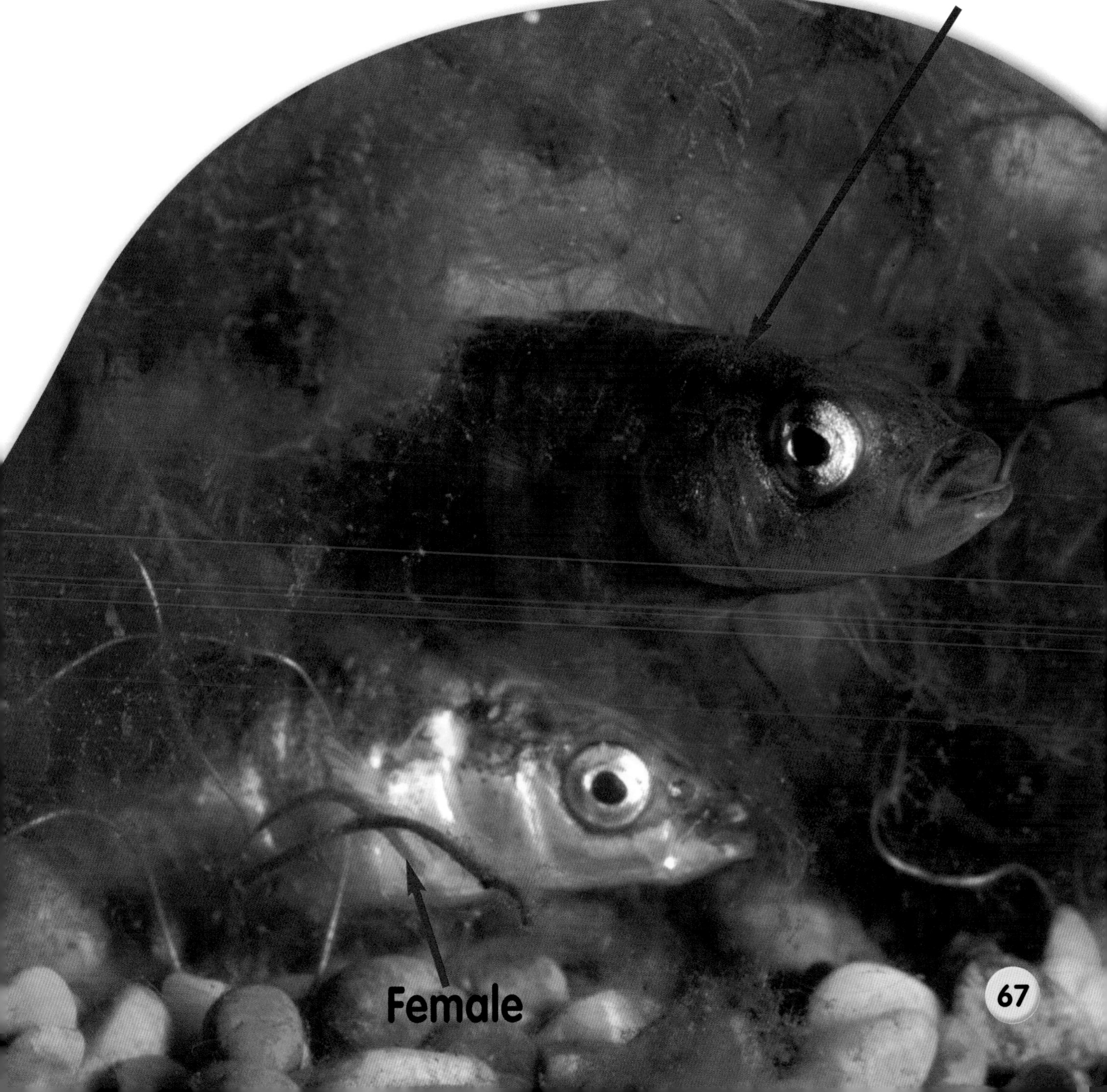

AMAZING FISH FACT
The male stickleback guards the eggs in his nest and looks after the young when they hatch.

Male

Female

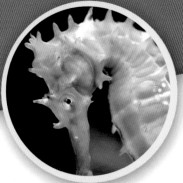

Seahorses

This very unusual looking fish has a horse-like head and a tail it can use to hold onto things. The seahorse can move each of its eyes separately – one can look forwards while the other looks backwards.

The seahorse's body is covered in armour made of hard, bony sections.

Before they mate, the male and female seahorses hold each other's tail, swim side-by-side, or swing around on a piece of seaweed together.

Most types of seahorse pair for life.

68

The male seahorse has a pouch on his tummy. The pouch is a bit like a pocket. The female lays her eggs inside the pouch and the male seahorse carries the eggs.

When the babies hatch, the male gives birth. He holds onto a piece of seaweed with his long tail. He rocks backwards and forwards until the babies pop out of his pouch. This can last for about two days.

Baby seahorse

Pouch

AMAZING FISH FACT
Seahorses can change colour to match their surroundings.

Reptile & Amphibian Families

What is a reptile?

A reptile is an animal with a thick skin covered in scales. Reptiles are **ectothermic**. This means that their body temperature goes up or down with the temperature of the air or water around them.

This is a crocodile's foot – you can see its scaly skin.

Snakes, lizards, crocodiles, alligators, tortoises and turtles are all reptiles.

Snakes are reptiles with no legs.

Scales

Every few months, a snake wriggles out of its old skin. A shiny, new skin, a size bigger, has grown underneath.

Old skin

Lizards are reptiles. Most lizards have four legs and a tail.

If a predator, such as a bird, grabs a lizard's tail, the tip breaks off. The bird is left with the twitching tail. The lizard runs away and soon grows a new tail!

AMESSING REPTILE FACT
Giant Galapagos tortoises can live to be over 100 years old!

This agama lizard is growing a new tail – the tip is missing.

Tortoises and turtles are reptiles with shells.

A giant Galapagos tortoise

Reptile life

This emerald tree boa gives birth to live babies.

Adult reptiles usually live on their own. Males and females get together to **mate** and then separate again. After mating most female reptiles lay eggs, but some reptiles give birth to live babies.

Chameleons are tree lizards that can change their skin colour! The female shows the male she is ready to mate by changing colour.

AMAZING REPTILE FACT

Reptile eggs feel rubbery. The shell is softer than a bird's egg, but strong.

A pair of chameleons.

Female

Reptiles lay lots of eggs in one go. Only a few hatch – the rest are often eaten by other animals.

Male

Female pythons coil their bodies around their eggs to keep them warm.

Most reptile mums leave their eggs to hatch on their own, but some reptiles look after their eggs.

When a baby reptile hatches it looks like a tiny copy of its parents. The baby is ready to find its own food right away. Baby snakes can hunt as soon as they are born.

Egg

This western pond turtle has just hatched.

What is an amphibian?

This is a toad. It looks like a frog, but has drier, bumpier skin.

An amphibian is an animal that lives in water and on land. Like reptiles, amphibians are ectothermic. Their bodies are the same temperature as the air or water around them. Amphibians have smooth skins.

Frogs, toads, newts, salamanders and caecilians are all amphibians.

This is a caecilian. It has no legs, and looks like a snake.

Newts and salamanders are amphibians with tails.

This is a fire salamander.

Most amphibians like warm, damp places with plenty of plants they can use as hiding places.

Frogs and toads are amphibians with no tails.

The bright blue colour of this poison arrow frog tells predators, "Stay away – I'm poisonous".

Amphibian life

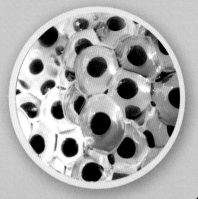

Amphibian eggs have no shells. A frog's eggs look like jelly.

Adult amphibians usually live on their own. Males and females get together to mate. After mating, female amphibians lay eggs. Most amphibians lay their eggs in water. This stops the eggs drying out.

In the spring, male and female frogs and toads go to ponds to mate. Then the females lay eggs.

AMAZING AMPHIBIAN FACT
Male frogs puff out their throats to sing a croaky song. This attracts females.

Baby amphibians hatch from eggs. They have large heads, long tails and breathe through **gills**, like fish. Soon they grow legs and begin breathing with lungs. Then they can live on land.

These are the young of a spotted salamander.

Most amphibians don't look after their eggs or babies, but there are some amazing amphibian parents.

Eggs

Some poison arrow frogs lay their eggs in water-filled hollows in trees. They carry the tadpoles to a new home if the water dries out.

The male midwife toad carries his eggs on his back until they hatch.

In this section we are going to find out about some amazing life cycles – from the giant Komodo dragon to the tiny red-eyed tree frog.

Komodo dragon

Red-eyed tree frog

Amazing reptile and amphibian life cycles

1 **A pair of rattlesnakes**

A male and female snake meet and mate.

SNAKE LIFE CYCLE

All reptiles have a life cycle with these stages.

4 **A young emerald tree boa**

Baby snakes are ready to go off on their own as soon as they hatch or are born.

2 **A female corn snake**

The female lays eggs. Some snakes give birth to live babies.

3 **A baby ball python**

Baby snakes hatch from the eggs.

1 A male and a female frog meet and mate.

2 The female lays hundreds of eggs in water.

5 The baby frogs leave the water. They grow bigger and bigger.

FROG LIFE CYCLE
Most amphibians have a life cycle with these stages.

4 Over several weeks the tadpoles grow legs and lungs for breathing air on land. They lose their tails.

3 Tadpoles with tails hatch from the eggs. They swim in the water and breathe through gills, like fish.

AMAZING REPTILE FACT

This male Jackson's chameleon uses his horns to fight other males for females.

A crocodile can bite
but it cannot chew.

Nile crocodiles

Nile crocodiles live beside lakes and rivers in Africa. They wait for big animals such as antelopes to come for a drink, then they grab them and eat them! Nile crocodiles also eat monkeys, turtles, birds and fish.

After about 60 days the eggs hatch.

After she has mated, the female crocodile makes a nest beside the river. She lays between 50 and 60 eggs.

Baby crocodile

AMAZING REPTILE FACT
A male Nile crocodile can grow to six metres long.

Crocodiles are fierce, but they are very good mums. They guard their eggs and even help break open the eggs with their mouths so the babies can get out.

The baby crocodiles call to their mum to let her know they are hatching.

The female looks after the babies in the shallow water of the river. After about eight weeks the babies go off on their own.

The female gently carries the babies from the nest to the river in her mouth.

Green turtles

The green turtle lives in warm oceans. Green turtles eat underwater plants, such as sea grass. Female green turtles go to the same beach every year to mate and lay eggs.

An adult green turtle can weigh 200 kilograms.

Turtles swim by paddling with their flippers.

AMAZING REPTILE FACT

Some females swim about 1,000 kilometres to get to their breeding beach. It can take them weeks!

The adult male and female turtles meet and mate in the shallow water.

Flipper

The green turtle lays up to 200 eggs.

The female turtle digs a deep hole in the sand with her flippers. She lays her eggs, covers them with sand, and then crawls back to the sea.

The baby turtles hatch after about seven weeks. The babies have to look after themselves. They dig out of the sand and dash to the sea.

The tiny turtle hatchlings are in danger of being eaten by predators, such as seabirds.

**The dragon's spit is so
full of germs, just one
bite can kill its prey.**

Komodo dragons

The Komodo dragon is the world's largest lizard. These giant reptiles live on Komodo Island and two other islands in South East Asia. Komodo dragons hunt for wild pigs and deer. They also eat animals that are already dead.

Male Komodos stand on their back legs to wrestle, to attract a mate.

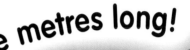

An adult male can be three metres long!

After mating, the female scrapes out a shallow nest in the ground and lays about 25 eggs. The female then leaves the eggs to hatch on their own.

The dragon's eggs hatch after seven to nine months. The babies climb trees and eat insects and lizards. Trees are safe, because if an adult dragon catches a baby, it will eat it!

This baby dragon is two days old and about 30 centimetres long.

AMAZING REPTILE FACT

A female Komodo dragon in a British zoo laid eggs that hatched into babies even though she had no male around to mate with!

Red-eyed tree frogs

The red-eyed tree frog lives in **rainforests** in Central America. It is a nocturnal frog. This means it rests during the day, and is active at night. Red-eyed tree frogs eat insects.

The frog's toes have suction pads to help it stick to leaves.

In the breeding season, male red-eyed tree frogs gather together on branches over a pond.

AMAZING AMPHIBIAN FACT

With its eyes closed the frog blends into its green habitat. If attacked, it opens its big red eyes – this startles predators!

The males call to females with a clicking noise.

This parrot snake is eating a red-eyed tree frog's eggs.

After mating, the female lays up to 50 eggs on a leaf that's hanging over the pond. Laying lots of eggs in one go means at least some babies will survive.

After about five days the eggs hatch and the tadpoles fall down into the pond below.

Tadpole

When these tadpoles have grown into frogs, they will climb back into the trees.

89

Darwin's frogs

The Darwin's frog lives near rivers in damp, shady, mountain forests in South America. Darwin's frogs eat insects and small animals, such as worms. The males are very good father

This frog has an unusual pointy, wobbly section on the end of its nose!

When a female Darwin's frog has laid her eggs, the male guards them. After about two weeks, the babies inside the eggs start to move. Now the male picks up the eggs with his tongue and puts them into his mouth.

The eggs are in here!

The male puts up to 15 eggs into a pouch in his mouth.

The tadpoles hatch inside the male's mouth. They stay in his mouth for 50 days feeding on their egg yolks. When they have grown into little froglets, the babies climb out of dad's mouth!

An adult Darwin's frog is just 2.5 centimetres long!

Froglet

That's amazing!

Are you ready for some more amazing reptile and amphibian facts? Did you know there's a toad that doesn't have tadpoles; a snake that's as long as six men; and a lizard that's a left-over from prehistoric times?

The North American bullfrog lays 25,000 eggs in one go!

These men are carrying an anaconda.

The anaconda is the world's heaviest snake. It can weigh up to 250 kilograms and grow to 10 metres long.

The female anaconda gives birth to up to 80 babies in one go.

There are no tadpoles in the Surinam toad's life cycle.

The female Surinam toad lays her eggs and the male puts them onto her back. A protective covering of skin grows over the eggs. When the eggs hatch, baby toads break through the skin.

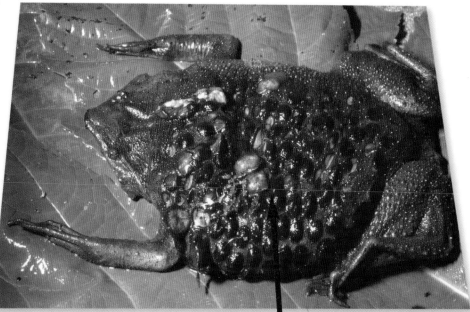

Eggs and baby toads

The tuatara is in a reptile family all of its own. Its closest relatives lived in prehistoric times, among the dinosaurs.

Baby tuataras do not hatch from their eggs for 12 to 15 months – the longest time of any reptile.

Glossary

amphibians – Cold blooded animals that lay its young in the water, but live on land when an adult.

ancestors – Parents, grandparents, great-grandparents – all the earlier individuals that came before.

breed – To mate and have babies.

burrow – Tunnels and holes under the ground where some animals live.

coast – The land along the seashore and the area around it.

colonies – Large groups.

coral reefs – Underwater places that look rocky but are actually made from the bodies of coral animals called polyps. The polyps have hard skeletons that join together. When a polyp dies, its skeleton stays as part of the reef, so the reefs get bigger and bigger.

courtship – Trying to win a mate.

den – A wild animal's home.

digested – When food is broken down in the stomach into materials that the body can then use to provide energy.

down – A bird's soft fine feathers.

ectothermic – An ectothermic animal needs sunshine to warm up and become active.

endothermic – Animals whose body temperature stays the same no matter how hot or cold the air or water is around them. You are endothermic!

fertilised – When a female egg is made to develop into a young animal.

flippers – Flat limbs that animals use to help them swim. Flippers don't have fingers, so the animal moves through the water easily. Seals and turtles have flippers.

freshwater – Water without salt in it. Most lakes are freshwater.

gills – Breathing organs (parts of the body) in animals that live in water.

grasslands – Wide open grassy spaces with few trees.

hatch – When a baby bird or animal breaks out of its egg.

herd – A group of animals that live together.

hollow – Something which is empty inside.

horns – These are bony growths that are found on the top of some animals heads. Horns can be used for fighting off other animals.

hunting – Going out and looking for prey to eat.

incubation – Keeping an egg warm after laying, and before it hatches.

mammals – Endothermic animals with hair, that feed their babies milk.

marsupial – An animal that has a pouch on the front of its body, which it carries its babies in. Kangaroos and koalas are marsupials.

mate – When a male and female animal meet and have babies.

migrates – Travels a long way to find food or a place to breed.

oxygen – A gas that all animals need to live.

pouch – This is the pocket-like part on the front of a marsupial, where the baby animal is carried.

predators – Animals which hunt and kill other animals for food.

prehistoric – A long time ago, before humans were alive.

prey – Animals which are hunted by other animals for food.

rainforests – Forests of tall trees in places with lots of rain.

reproduce – To have babies.

reptiles – Animals with scales such as snakes, lizards and crocodiles.

saltwater – Water with salt in it. The oceans are saltwater.

scales – Small, overlapping sections of hard skin that cover the bodies of fish.

shoal – A group of fish swimming together.

stages – Different times of an animal's life when the animal changes.

suckling – Feeding on mother's milk.

tailor – Someone who makes clothes.

temperature – How hot or cold something is.

territory – An area or place where an animal feeds and breeds.

tusks – Long, sharp pointed teeth.

upstream – The opposite direction to the flow of water in a river or stream.

Index

A
Africa 39, 40, 44, 82
African weaver birds 53
agama lizards 73
alligators 72
anacondas 92
angelfish 59, 60
anglerfish 62-63
antelopes 82
Arctic 44, 45
Arctic terns 44-45
Asia 39, 40, 48, 86

B
bald eagles 37
ball pythons 80
black tip sharks 61
blue-footed booby 35
bower birds 46-47
butterfly fish 58

C
caecilians 76
chameleons 74
corn snakes 80
courtship 50, 94
crocodiles 72

D
Darwin's frogs 90-91
deer 86
dinosaurs 58, 93
duck-billed platypus 29
ducks 32

E
elephants 9
emerald tree boas 80
emperor penguins 42-43

F
fire salamanders 76
flamingos 5, 36
flower horn fish 60
frigate birds 35
frogs 5, 77, 78, 81

G
giant anteaters 16-17
giant Galapagos tortoises 73
gills 56, 79, 81, 94
giraffes 28, 29
grasslands 16
great white sharks 57, 58, 61
green turtles 84-85
grizzly bears 64

H
hammerhead sharks 58
hippopotamus 8, 24-25
hornbills 40-41
hummingbirds 33, 53

J
Jackson's chameleons 80

K
koalas 10, 26-27
Komodo dragons 86-87

L
lemon sharks 61
leopards 8
life cycle diagrams 12-13,
    38-39, 60-61, 80-81
lionfish 60
lions 12-13, 23
lizards 40, 72, 73, 74, 86, 87

M
marsupials 26, 95
meerkats 10, 20-21
midwife toads 79
migration 44
monkeys 82

N
newts 76
Nile crocodiles 82-83
North American bullfrogs 92
nurse sharks 61

O
orcas 11, 18-19
ostriches 33, 53

P
parrot snakes 89
peacocks 34
peahens 34
pipistrelle bats 9, 14-15
poison arrow frogs 77, 79
polar bears 28
predators 21, 23, 51, 64, 73,
    77, 85, 88, 95
puffins 50-51
pythons 80

R
rattlesnakes 80
red-eyed tree frogs 88-89
robins 38-39

S
salamanders 76
salmon 60, 64-65
seahorses 4, 68-69
sharks 57, 61
shoals 56, 58, 95
snakes 40, 72, 75, 76, 80
spotted salamanders 79
sticklebacks 66-67
storks 36
Surinam toads 93
swallows 52
swans 34, 36

T
tadpoles 5, 79, 81, 89, 91, 92,
    93
tailorbirds 48-49
territory 34, 95
toads 76, 77, 78, 93
tortoises 72, 73
tuataras 93
turtles 72, 73, 82

W
wagtails 52
warthogs 11, 22-23
Western pond turtles 75
wild pigs 86
woodpeckers 37